PLAY BALL!

A Hello Reader! Activity Book

ISBN 0-590-52761-4

Written by Gina Shaw
Illustrated by Joan Holub

12 11 10 9/9 0/0

Printed in the U.S.A. 23

First Scholastic printing, April 1995

SCHOLASTIC INC.

New York Toronto London Auckland Sydney

All Kinds of Balls

Pam and Ben Bear like to play ball. One ball in each row is not like the others. Cross out the one that does not belong.

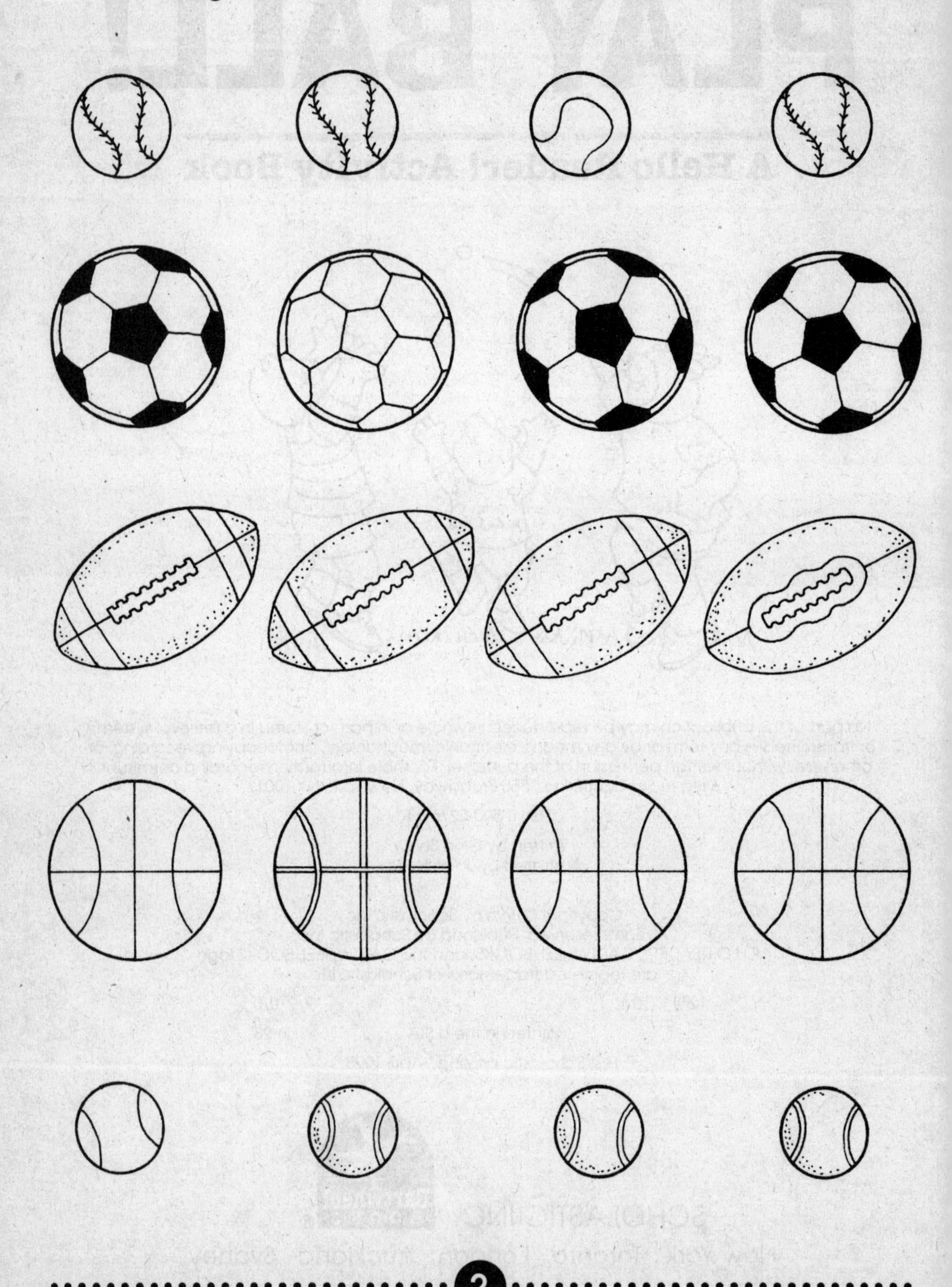

Things to Play With

Look at all of the things on this page! Circle the ones that can be used when you play ball.

Who Plays What?

Pam, Ben, Meg and their friends are dressed to play ball. Draw a line from each bear to the kind of ball he or she plays.

M

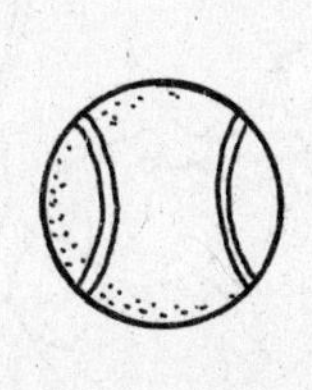

Name That Game

The Bear family is at a ball game. Look at the words on the signs. Circle these words in the puzzle. The words go up and down and across.

There are two words in the puzzle that tell the name of this game. Put the words together. Write the word here. ________________________________

Shooting Hoops

Pam, Ben, and their friends are shooting baskets. Follow each path to a basket. Use a different color for each bear.

Now, count the number of basketballs on each path. This tells you how many each bear got in the basket. Who won? Put a check next to that bear.

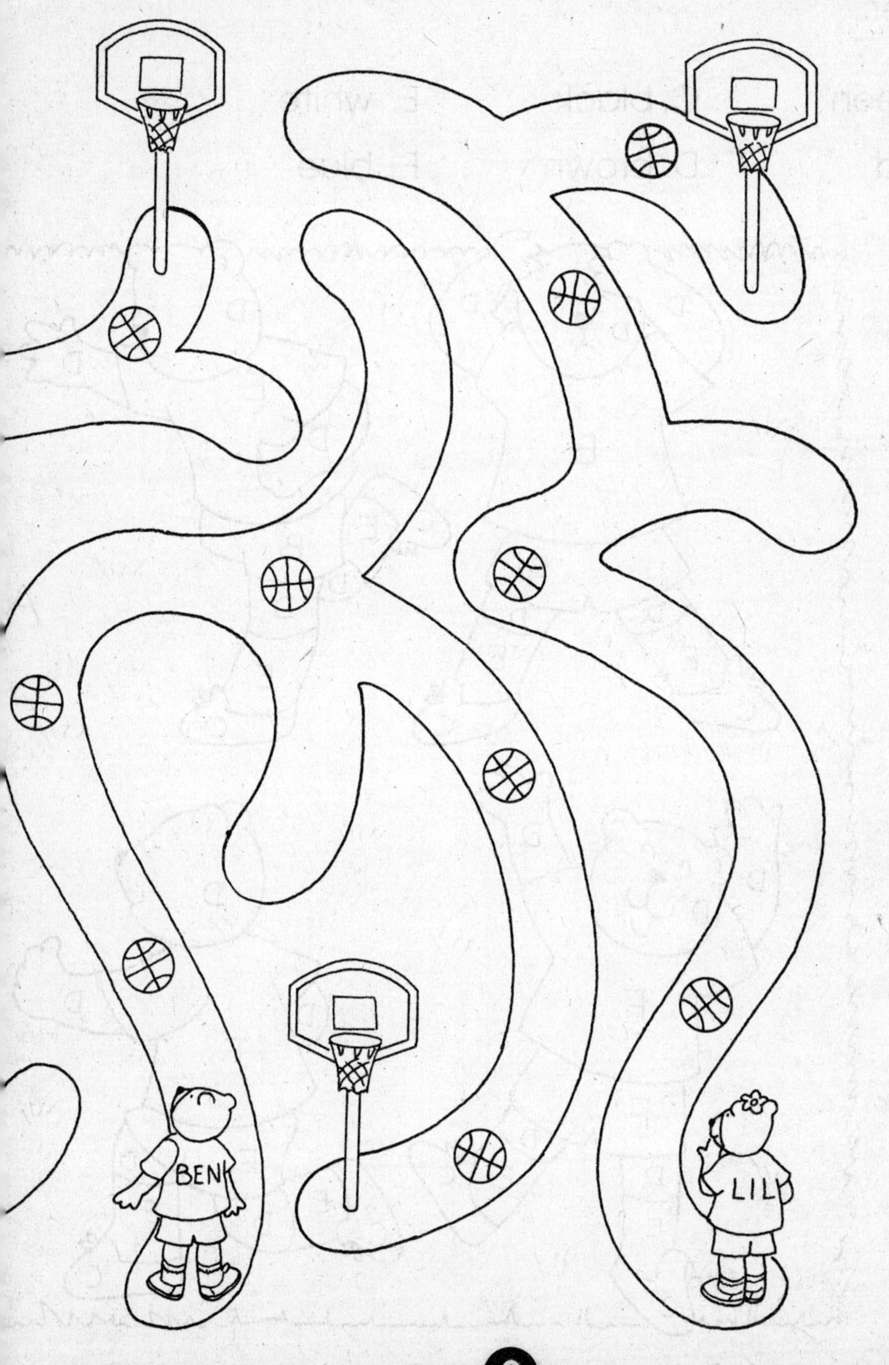

A Hidden Picture

One of these players is not part of a team. Color this picture to find out who it is. Use these colors. Fill in each letter with the correct color. Then circle the player.

A. green C. black E. white

B. red D. brown F. blue

One Ball, Many Games

Pam, Ben, and Meg have one small ball. But, they can play many games with it. Look at each picture. Read the names of the games. On the blank line, write the letter of the name that goes with each game.

A. Hit the Penny

B. Bear in the Middle

C. Playing Catch

D. Paw Ball

1. ____________

2. ______________

3. ____________

4. ______________

What's Wrong Here?

These bears are playing tennis. But five things are wrong with this picture. Circle each one of them.

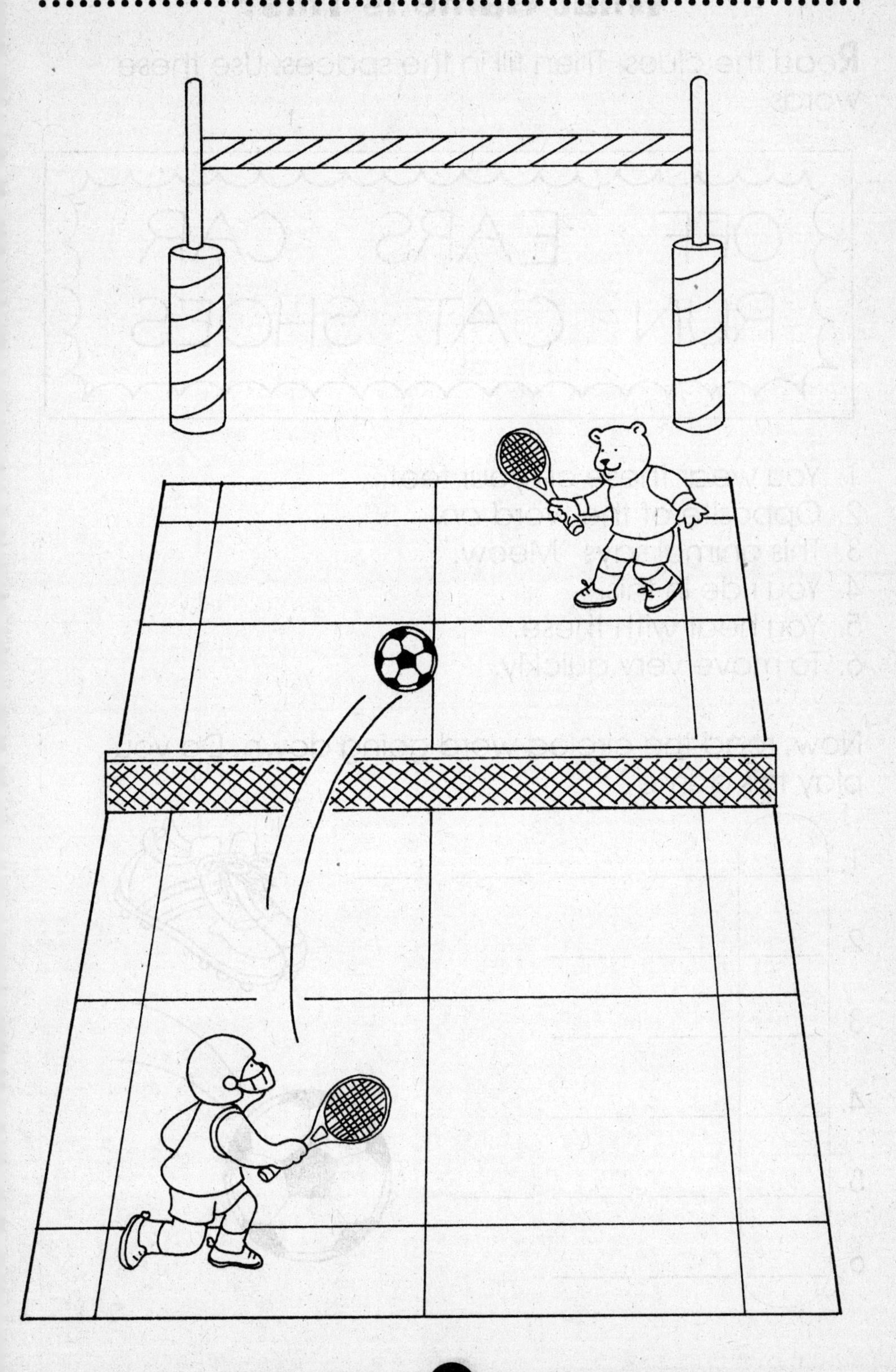

What Game is This?

Read the clues. Then fill in the spaces. Use these words.

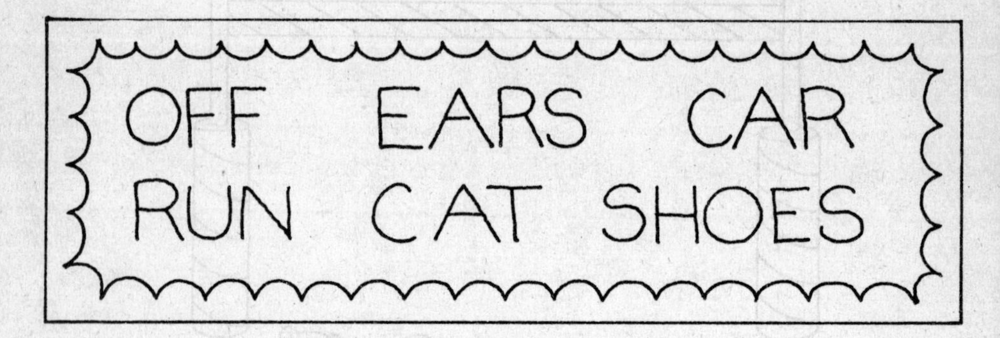

1. You wear these on your feet.
2. Opposite of the word *on*.
3. This animal says "Meow."
4. You ride in this.
5. You hear with these.
6. To move very quickly.

Now, read the circled word going down. Do you play this game?

A Fill-in Story

Pam plays soccer. Here is her story. Read each sentence. Circle the correct word.

1. Pam has a soccer _______.
   ball   bell

2. She kicks it with her ______.
   fin   foot

3. Pam gets it in the ______.
   net   not

4. She loves to ______ soccer.
   plant   play

5. Pam's team ______!
   white   wins

Up, Up, and Away

What is happening in this picture? Connect the dots. Follow the letters in alphabetical order.

A
B
C
D
E
F
G
H
I
J
K
L
M
N
O
P
Q
R
S
T
U
V
W
X
Y
Z
3
8
16

Beach Fun

How many beach balls can you find in this picture? Color all of them. Use bright colors!

Answers

Page 2

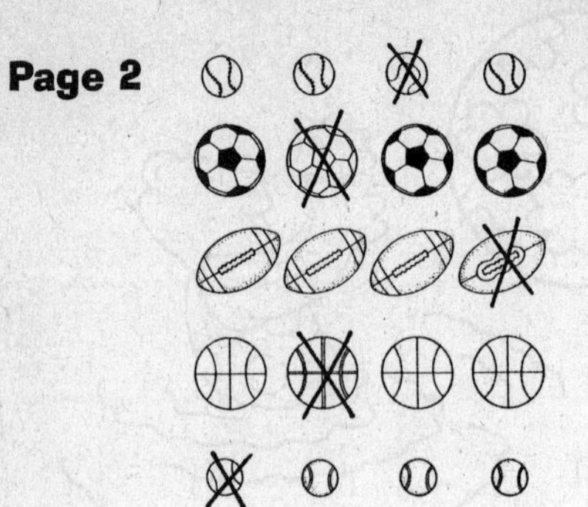

Page 3

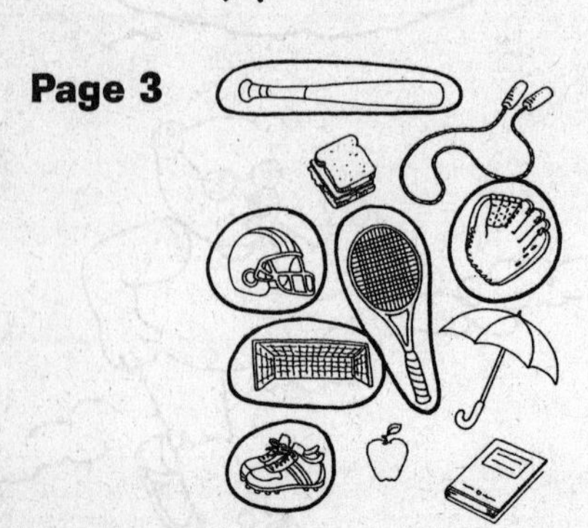

Pages 4–5

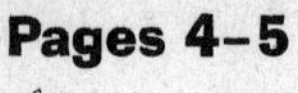

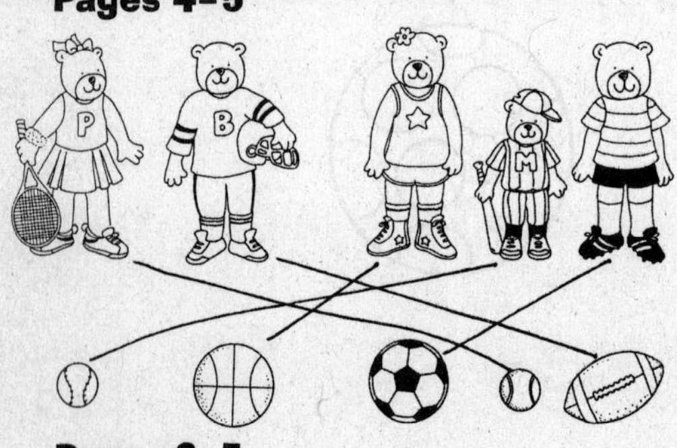

Pages 6–7

BASEBALL

Pages 8–9

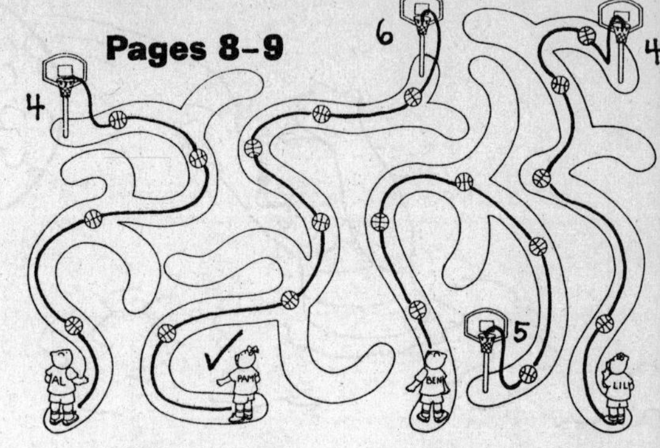

Pages 10–11

Pages 12–13

1. B
2. A
3. D
4. C

Pages 14–15

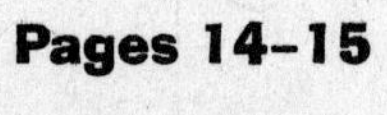

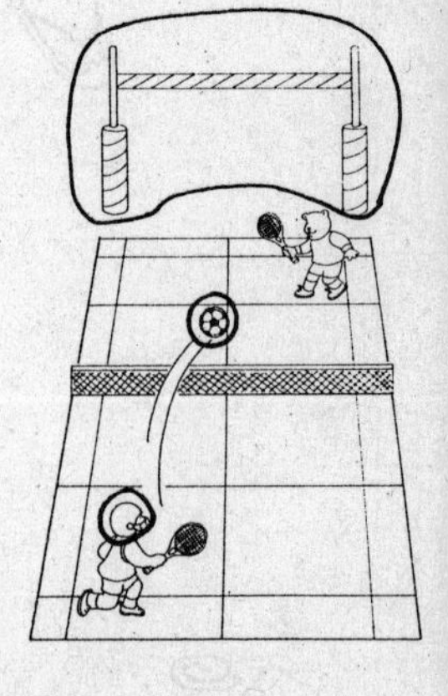

Answers

Page 16

1. SHOES
2. OFF
3. CAT
4. CAR
5. EARS
6. RUN

Page 17

1. ball
2. foot
3. net
4. play
5. wins

Pages 18-19

Pages 20-21

You should have colored these four beach balls.

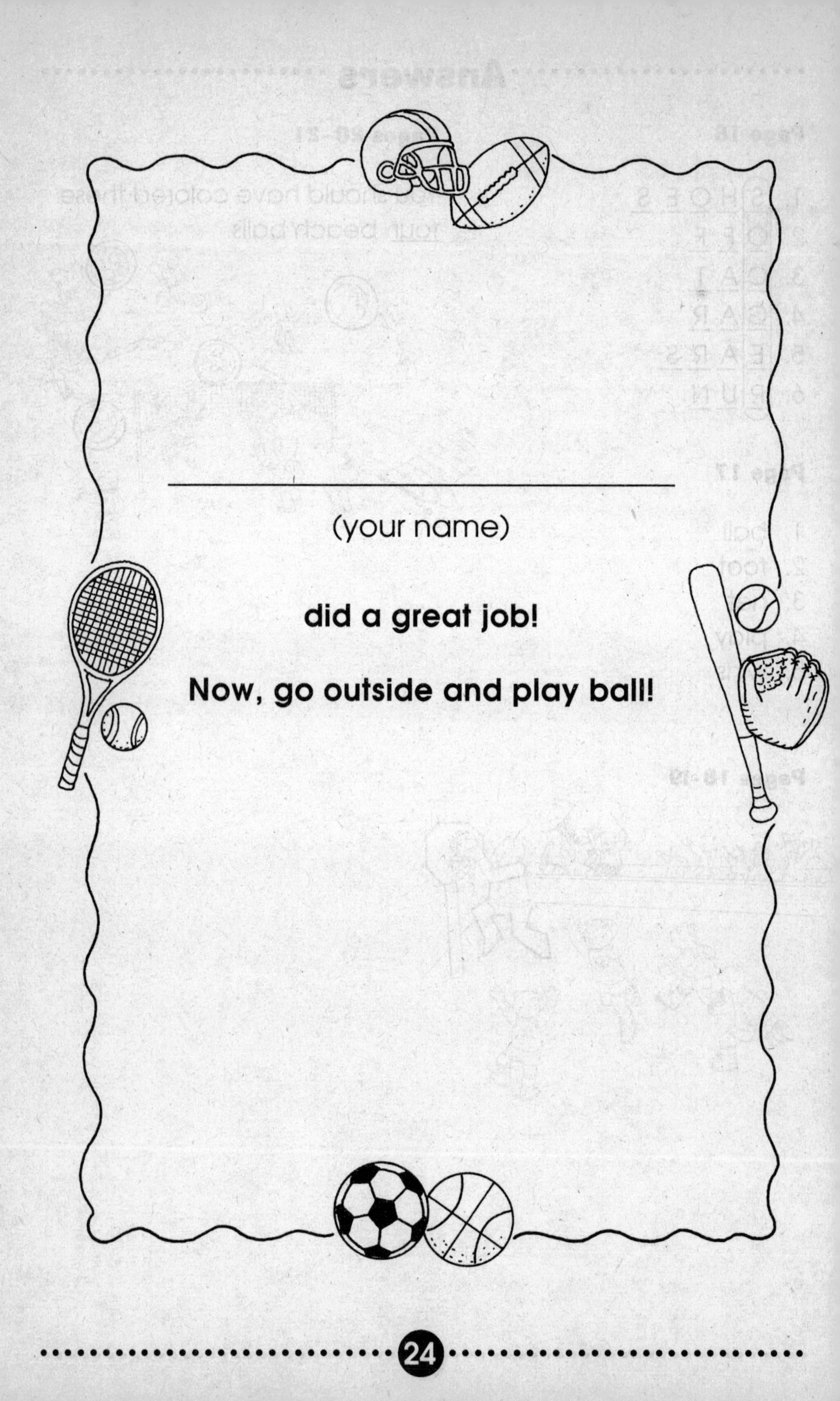

(your name)

did a great job!

Now, go outside and play ball!